LANDS OF
MYSTERY
◁ MYTHS AND LEGENDS ▷

Translated by Frances Halton

Text by Gilles Ragache

Illustrations by Michael Welply

Series edited by Gilles Ragache

CHERRYTREE BOOKS

A Cherrytree Book

Adapted by A S Publishing
from *Terres de Mystère*
published by Hachette
© 1993, Hachette, Paris

First published 1995
by Cherrytree Press Ltd
a subsidiary of
The Chivers Company Ltd
Windsor Bridge Road
Bath, Avon BA2 3AX

British Library Cataloguing in Publication Data
Ragache, Gilles
    Lands of Mystery.—(Myths and Legends Series)
    I. Halton, Frances II. Ragache, Gilles
    III. Series
    398-2452974446

    ISBN 0-7451-5261-9

Printed in Hong Kong by Colorcraft Ltd

▷ CONTENTS ◁

EGYPT

MYSTERIOUS PUNT

A large crowd watched as three heavily laden ships approached the shore. Suddenly a cry went up: 'They are Knemhotep's ships!'

Two years earlier, Knemhotep had set off to the mysterious land of Punt, and since then nothing had been heard of him. The crowd grew until it spread as far as the eye could see. A little to one side waited a group of important people, including several princesses and even some great priests from the Nile Valley. Everyone was certain that the ships were bringing back great treasures, for Knemhotep had already made ten other voyages to Punt in his long sailing ships, and in spite of all the dangers he had met these had been successful.

The priests had helped Knemhotep to mount his expedition in the hope that he would bring back the incense used in their secret ceremonies. Incense from Punt was the best of all. It came in the form of amber-yellow resin. The princesses hoped they would be able to buy fine red powder, of higher quality than the red kermes dye they used for make-up in Egypt.

When the ships at last reached shore everyone crowded round, though few could afford to buy!

The guards had to intervene to establish order. As well as incense and powder, Knemhotep had brought back treasures from far-off Punt that caught the imagination of even the most sober Egyptians. For days his customers disputed the price of myrrh, fine silks, exotic spices, tortoise-shell and ingots of precious metal. The richest even wanted to buy three slaves whom the prince of Punt had given Knemhotep in exchange for three brooches of lapis-lazuli.

'Where is Punt? Now you are growing old surely you can tell us?' the friends of the old sailor asked each time he came back. But Knemhotep's only answer was an enigmatic smile, and the simple direction, 'South!' Punt lay hidden, far beyond the seas. Knemhotep would not say more. For thirty years he had told no one his secret, not even the high priest. For there lay his strength; as long as he kept quiet no one could take his place and it was in everyone's interest to keep him alive. But if he died, the route to Punt would be lost with him.

Sometimes Knemhotep would talk about Punt, without giving away where it was. There, he said, a king and queen decked with gold and precious stones reigned over a people with dark skins. Their nobles lived in a vast stone palace surrounded with gardens filled with exotic flowers and dog-headed monkeys. They traded thick spotted furs, myrrh and blue and green precious stones with Knemhotep.

This time Knemhotep was worn out on his return. But he had no regrets. Eleven such voyages had made him fabulously rich, and this last voyage had been the most successful of all. Next time the waters of the Nile rose, he would return to his birthplace, Elephantine Island, beside the great river. And there he would stay for ever.

Knemhotep the Egyptian grew rich on goods
brought back from the land of Punt, but
would never say where it was.

5

▷ THE FIVE WORLDS ◁

A little black dugout canoe bobbed slowly on the muddy waters of the river Atoyoc. In it were two young Indians who leaned casually over the water. Every now and then they swiftly and surely harpooned fish that swam near the surface.

Like most Indians, Xica and Ulque were inquisitive. The night before, as they sat round the fire, they had listened to the elders telling tales of the strange countries that stretched to the edge of the world. Xica was too young to understand what they were saying, and had fallen asleep. So now he asked his brother to tell him about these far-off lands.

'What lies beyond the horizon?' asked Xica.

'Which horizon do you mean?' replied Ulque. 'There are at least four – one in each direction!'

Xica was rather surprised. 'I know that. But surely it's the same in every direction?' he asked.

'Certainly not!' said Ulque. 'The four worlds are entirely different.'

'Different how?'

'Different colours, to start with.'

'How do you know?' breathed Xica, who was fascinated and longed to know more.

'I know because the elders tell about it. Last night they were saying how, long ago, seven warriors of the tribe had been blown far to the east by a storm.'

'And what did they see there?' asked Xica, more and more intrigued.

'A red world!' said Ulque, as he speared a fish, stunned it and lifted it off his spear. 'A black and red world, like the night and the rising sun.'

'Is it like our world, but red?' asked Xica.

While they fish, Xica and Ulque talk over the tales of the elders.

6

'Not really, because it is the world of youth. The gods live there – they are red too – and they stay young for ever.'

'What do they do?'

'They sing and dance all day. When they are hungry, they eat spears of corn which grow there untended.'

'Does anyone else live there?'

'Yes, according to the elders, the rain god lives there, hidden in a vast garden.'

'What's the garden called?'

Ulque thought for a moment. 'Tlaalocan, I think. No one has ever seen it because it is surrounded by huge rose bushes.'

Xica thought for a few minutes before asking:

'What happens to the south?'

Ulque realized that he would have to repeat everything he had heard the night before.

'A blue world, covered with flowers and fruit. Thousands of birds live there.'

'Who lives with the birds?'

'The sun! It spends every day high in the sky there, giving out so much heat that the blue world is also the land of fire.'

The blue land of the south, where lived the sun and brilliantly coloured birds.

Xica and Ulque chattered and fished for a long time, until the sun was sinking in the west and they had to think of going home.

'What happens there?' asked Xica, pointing towards the setting sun.

'The white world. A long time ago, a deep hole opened in the ground there, like an enormous cavern.'

'Who lives there?'

'Women! That's where human children come from. It's a world of mothers, dressed all in white, who wait on the goddess of flowers.'

'What does the sun do when it goes to the white world?'

'It spends every night resting in a huge house built of earth and stone in the heart of the white world.'

The next question soon came.

'What about the north?'

'To the north lies a frozen desert that is so dark and dangerous that no one has ever come back from it.'

'Why not?'

'Because fierce demons called Mimixcoa live there. They wander through the cactuses searching for prey. Their chief has white hair and his whole body is painted black. He is dressed in black from head to foot, and he reigns over the land of nine plains where dead warriors go to carry on their battles.'

'How do you know when you are getting near the land of the nine plains?' asked Xica uneasily.

'When you see a huge black eagle gliding over your head; it warns the Mimixcoa of all strangers who want to enter their country. Then you must turn back.'

Now Xica was frightened. He was quiet for a moment, then said:

'So there are altogether four worlds?'

'Well, not exactly,' said Ulque. 'There is also a fifth world, in the centre.'

The chief of the Mimixcoa prowls the frozen land of the north.

'Where is the centre?' asked Xica, perplexed.

Ulque had no idea. But he did know that at the centre of the centre was an amazing tree – a tree of many colours, which never stopped growing and on which perched a giant bird.

'Have you seen it?'

'No, but the elders' ancestors saw it.'

'And which world are we in?'

Ulque thought for a while, speared a last fish, and then turned to his brother.

'I don't know. Somewhere in the five worlds, I suppose!'

AUSTRALIA

THE LAND OF FLOWERS

Long, long ago life in Australia was happy and carefree, watched over by the great and wise magician Bayamie. Each year he made the clouds give rain in winter, the trees grow green in spring and the fruit ripen in summer. But Bayamie grew old and one sad day he left the earth for Bullimah, a valley far beyond the Ubi-Ubi mountains, and no one ever saw him again.

Without Bayamie to oversee things, the leaves fell from the trees, flowers faded, and rivers dwindled to muddy trickles. The earth became sad and dusty, and people grew very hungry. Every evening they prayed and sang in the great desert, hoping for Bayamie's return. But Bayamie could not hear them. Daydreaming on a crystal throne, far out of reach of human voices, he had no idea what was happening. Little by little his feet turned into crystal and return to the earth was impossible.

One evening three young magicians called Buan, Burra and Bailli made a circle of white stones and lit a great fire in its centre. The wind carried its flames so high into the sky that they caught Bayamie's attention. Now they could get in touch with him by their thoughts.

Bayamie promised to help. Every morning from the next day on, three sturdy trees that had withstood the drought were thickly covered with a sweet-tasting substance like white snow. But three months later this ceased to appear. Buan, Burra and Bailli tried to make contact with Bayamie again, but they had no success.

A great council was called and in the end it was agreed that it would be best to go to Bayamie and explain face to face what was

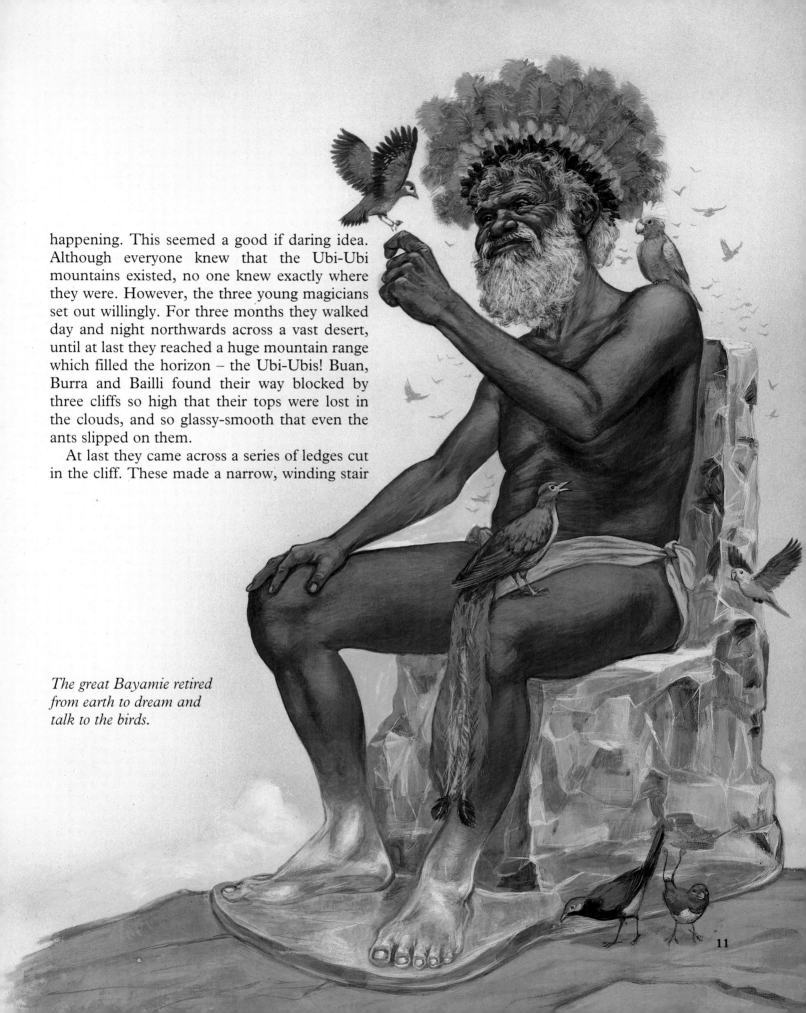

happening. This seemed a good if daring idea. Although everyone knew that the Ubi-Ubi mountains existed, no one knew exactly where they were. However, the three young magicians set out willingly. For three months they walked day and night northwards across a vast desert, until at last they reached a huge mountain range which filled the horizon – the Ubi-Ubis! Buan, Burra and Bailli found their way blocked by three cliffs so high that their tops were lost in the clouds, and so glassy-smooth that even the ants slipped on them.

At last they came across a series of ledges cut in the cliff. These made a narrow, winding stair

The great Bayamie retired from earth to dream and talk to the birds.

11

which led up and up towards the summit. They started on the dangerous climb. On and on, higher and higher they climbed. Four days and four nights later they reached the sky, full of white clouds.

The next day they came to the summit of mount Ubi. It was a huge, flat, deserted plateau. There was no trace of Bayamie, nor any sign of the flowers and trees of Bullimah. The magicians, tired and disappointed, were wondering whether to start the long climb back when they heard the sound of running water. They traced it to a large boulder, beside which a spring made a sparkling pool. The magicians drank deep and then bathed their aching limbs in the cool water. Their spirits rose and their strength came back. They made a circle of white stones on the ground, lit a fire in its centre and chanted all night, calling on Bayamie.

Early in the morning a deep voice answered them. The clouds parted and they saw Bayamie, sitting on his crystal throne.

'What are you doing here? How dare you disturb me?' he thundered.

'We want to tell you what is happening on earth,' replied Buan.

The old magician was appalled to hear how people, animals and plants were suffering. He had thought that he had made all well. He listened carefully, asked a number of questions, and then gave an order in a language the three could not understand. Three servants appeared, with torches in their hands. One stood by Buan, one by Burra and the third by Bailli.

'Follow them, and take care not to get lost. I can do no more for you,' said Bayamie. And the servants guided the three magicians towards the grey sky. A gap opened in the clouds before them and closed after them. After a long time they came out of the other side of the clouds, into brilliant light and colour. They had reached Bullimah. All the flowers in the world grew in this lost valley, and rainbows arched above it. The air was warm and sweetly scented. Buan, Burra and Bailli gathered great armfuls of flowers to take back to earth.

Their guides led them back again through the clouds to the top of the steep staircase. The way down seemed to take for ever but at last they felt firm ground beneath their feet. Immediately they scattered their flowers in the wind, and wherever they landed they took root and began to grow.

But Buan, Burra and Bailli had forgotten to mention water! Before long all the flowers were beginning to wilt. Fortunately Bayamie sent bees to see that all was well, and they guided rainclouds to the young plants.

Since then drought has returned many times. But as long as Bayamie and his bees keep watch, spring will come again in Australia.

The young magicians brought back flowers from Bullimah and scattered them over the earth.

CHINA
MOUNT KUNLUN

The gods of earth were growing old. At last they decided to seek help from the Empress of the West, who lived on the summit of Kunlun, a mountain so high that it reached the stars. It was surrounded by foaming seas on which nothing – not even a goose feather – could float. Even a child could not stand on the quicksands of its shores.

Mount Kunlun was made up of nine tiers, each surrounded by a thick wall, pierced by four gates. From the lowest gates flowed the four great rivers of China, from the highest gates came the winds and snowstorms. Sleek dragons kept watch at each gate, and many-coloured birds circled constantly round Kunlun, warning of any arrival. The gods of the earth decided to fly to Kunlun on the backs of great white birds, and after a long flight reached the mountain. At its very top they saw a magnificent palace, surrounded by a lake of jade-green water.

The empress was warned of the strangers' arrival by the harsh cries of her birds, but she ordered the dragons to allow the gods to enter. She smiled when she welcomed them, but did

not hide her surprise. 'Why have you dared to come here?' she asked. The youngest god spoke for all of them. 'Great Mother, we are worried – over the last few years we have begun to grow older. Do you know a cure for this?'

The empress invited her visitors to follow her to an orchard of magic trees unknown on earth. Among them was a peach tree. It was 6000 years old, but it had not flowered for 59 centuries. Perhaps if they waited a little?

The gods, full of hope, settled down to wait and a hundred years later a flower appeared on the tree. The next day another unfolded, and in the end the tree was covered with fruit. Then the gods ate the precious peaches, and as they tasted them their wrinkles and grey hair disappeared. Young and beautiful once more, they thanked their hostess a thousand times, mounted their great white birds, and flew singing back to earth. Bent over their paddy fields, the peasants heard them. They worked hard and grew older day by day. They had no hope of tasting the peaches of immortality!

The ageing gods fly in to Mount Kunlun in the mountains of the far west.

15

IRELAND

THE LAND OF SHADOWS

For many years, Cuchulain had loved Emer, the beautiful daughter of King Forgall. He longed to marry her but the King said that first Cuchulain must prove himself. He challenged Cuchulain to go to the fortress of Skathach the sorceress, in the heart of the mysterious Land of Shadows.

As night fell, he set out alone in his father's old leather coracle, heading due north. Foam-capped waves tossed the little boat like a cork on the empty sea, but with great skill he held his course. When dawn came he scanned the horizon for land, and was almost despairing when, as light strengthened, he made out the coast of the Land of Shadows.

Cuchulain made his landing on the shore of an inlet. Black rocks towered over him, and the fine sandy shore was just as black. Although it was now midday, the sun had hardly risen above the horizon and gleamed only fitfully through the mists. Cuchulain paused to find his bearings. He looked up at the sky, and then walked resolutely towards a thick forest. The trees grew so densely that he had to hack out a path with his sword in near darkness.

Suddenly men dressed all in black sprang up before him – armed giants, followed by dwarfs. When Cuchulain attacked them, they vanished as his weapon touched them, for they were just illusions. The Land of Shadows was well named!

The next day the forest thinned out and Cuchulain found himself in a vast, rocky desert. Tormented by hunger and thirst, he stumbled on. At midday, he made out at last the shape of a huge building surrounded by a grassy plain; it was Skathach's fortress. Cuchulain's heart lifted and he hurried on. But as soon as he stepped on to the plain, the ground gave beneath him and he felt as if he were being sucked into the centre of the earth. Any movement only caused him to sink deeper.

The mud had reached his thighs when he thought of flinging himself down full length and crawling back. It took him an hour to regain firm ground. Before he had time to recover, a strange youth appeared in a halo of light. His face shone like the sun. 'Who are you?' asked Cuchulain, grasping his sword.

Cuchulain sinks into the bog on his way to Skathach's fortress.

'That does not matter,' replied the stranger. 'I mean you no harm, and only want you to go on your way.'

'But how can I cross this bog? Even a bird would sink into it.'

'No one can cross it without my help.' And the stranger conjured up first a red apple, and then a huge wheel of stone and fire. The apple and the wheel floated in the air as if they were suspended between sky and earth.

'Follow wherever they lead, and you will reach Skathach's fortress.'

Before Cuchulain could answer, the stranger disappeared in a flash of lightning. The heavy stone wheel drew near to Cuchulain, and glowed red-hot; it began to revolve slowly and sank towards the ground. The apple spun in the air, tracing a path for the wheel. Where the wheel touched the marsh it smoked, hissed and hardened to form a narrow path firm enough to take the weight of a man. Cuchulain set out along it.

At last Cuchulain came to a rocky outcrop which bordered a deep ravine. At the bottom,

monstrous reptiles hissed and swarmed in seething water. On the other side was the inaccessible fortress of Skathach. Seated on the rocks was a group of young men, among whom were Cuchulain's friend Fierda and other brave Irish warriors who had long since vanished without trace. All had set out on a similar quest, and all had been frustrated close to success. From the walls of her fortress Skathach the sorceress mocked them.

The only way across the ravine was by a two-part bridge. It was made of a bendy substance,

Cuchulain uses the magic bridge to jump into the fortress.

and narrowed towards the centre where the two halves hardly touched. Cuchulain learned from his friends that the bridge tossed anyone who set foot on it into the air. The lucky ones fell on to the rocks; the others fell into the gorge to be eaten by the monsters.

Cuchulain was wondering what to do when the red apple span in front of him, and he felt an irresistible urge to bite into it. Immediately all his tiredness disappeared. He rushed on to the bridge and had just passed the centre when it threw him violently into the air. But Cuchulain was expecting this, and he used the thrust to catapult him forward in three somersaults to the gate of the fortress.

The magic apple had given Cuchulain the strength to carry out his jump, but the courage to make it was all his own. Skathach was so impressed that she allowed him to enter the fortress. He stayed there for a year and a day while the sorceress taught him many secrets that no one before him had been worthy to know.

He was sad to leave, but he knew that when he returned home he could at last marry Emer.

THE KINGDOM OF THE ELVES

One fine summer night, when young Bjorn was wandering through the great northern forest, he came across a group of elves dancing in the moonlight. For days he could think of nothing else. At last he asked his father where these strange creatures of the night lived. The old soldier hesitated, then said gravely:

'They live very far away, in a country from which there is no returning. Don't think about them any more.'

'But where is that country?' Bjorn insisted.

His father refused to tell him.

'At least tell me the name of their kingdom.'

'It's called Gimli. But you must promise never to try to go there.'

Bjorn promised at once, but he longed to know more. He decided to find out from his grandfather, who lived on the other side of the mountains. Before answering Bjorn's questions,

The home of the elves in frozen Gimli.

the old man cracked a few nuts and poked the fire thoughtfully.

'Your father is right. Gimli is very far away and no one can go there. It is in the heart of Bidblainn, the third sky.'

'The third sky?'

'Yes. The winds blow in the first sky, just over our heads where the clouds sail. The second sky, blue and grey, lies above the first. Only Yggdrasil, the magic tree at the heart of the world, crosses it. The third sky is higher still, at Yggdrasil's tip, near the sun; it is the home of light.'

Bjorn next asked what the home of the elves was like.

'It is a great wooden building. The elves gather in a huge room with a golden ceiling shining more brightly than the sun.'

'Do the elves live alone in Gimli?'

'No; their world is not far from Asgard and they belong to Freyr.'

The old man spoke this name reverently, for the god Freyr ruled over the sun, the rain and the plants, and brought people their harvests.

Bjorn had one last question.

'How does one get to Gimli?'

'That's impossible. To do so you must cross the great rainbow Bifrost. From time immemorial, no human has ever succeeded in reaching this magical kingdom.'

▷ BURDJOU ALAMASSI ◁

A thick layer of black lava crunched under the feet of the camels. Still warm, it covered the sand from sight. Nine Tuaregs, lost in a maze of deep gorges and steep ravines, slowly climbed the dried bed of the river Tarabin. Three months earlier they had set out to find Burdjou Alamassi, but as they journeyed they had become steadily weaker, their enthusiasm had waned, and their water reserves had dwindled. They were far from the caravan routes, for Burdjou Alamassi was well hidden.

The wadi became so steep that the Tuaregs had to dismount. Two of them, who were too exhausted to carry on, set up a camp and stayed there to look after the camels. The seven others wound their way through huge boulders and almost impenetrable thorny thickets. Then at dawn, the rising sun showed them the walls of a gleaming city: Burdjou Alamassi at last! Around it lay a lake of clear, mirror-smooth water – the last obstacle between them and their objective. The two strongest could not resist the tempta-

Roped together, the Tuaregs slither across the crystal lake.

tion to cross it at once; they dived in head first. There were two sharp snaps as their heads struck not water but crystal, and their necks were broken.

The rest of the group were horrified, but they would not give up now their goal was in sight. So the five men lowered themselves down a rope to the crystal surface and made their way gingerly across it. On the other side, their way was barred by a huge gate of bronze. The oldest, Hakkim, knocked seven times on the metal with the handle of his dagger. The heavy gates creaked open.

No one appeared on the threshold to welcome the travellers, and they made their way into an enormous empty hall. Its walls, entirely covered with diamonds, sparkled with a million points of light. Doors led off to a maze of similar rooms, where it was impossible to tell the difference between a reflection and a real person. Only three of the Tuareg, who had stayed in the first room, were able to find their way out; the other two were caught in the trap of light.

These three thought themselves safe until, as they set out on their way back, they were halted by a clear, sweet voice which begged them not to leave. They turned round to see a startlingly beautiful woman on the city wall: she was the princess of Hoggar, the sorceress of the Mountains of Light. Overwhelmed by her beauty, the two youngest turned back – and disappeared for ever. Only wise old Hakkim returned to the camp to join his last two companions and their camels, and eventually return home.

THE LAND OF FIRE

Coyote, the unchallenged chief of the powerful Wintu tribe, lived peacefully with his people on the banks of the Great Green River, until the day when the women came to ask him for fire. Coyote was very embarrassed, for at that time the Wintu had no fire, though everyone had heard tell of it.

'Why do you want fire? We have got on quite well without it all these years,' asked Coyote.

The women answered him eagerly, with a host of good reasons.

'So that we can cook our meat and fish, which is much better than eating them raw. So that we won't be so cold in winter. So that we can see at night.'

Coyote had to agree that their arguments were well founded. He would have liked to give them fire, but he had no idea where to get it.

'I'm sure you are right; let me think about this in peace and I'll find an answer', he replied, hoping to gain time.

The next day, while he was resting under a huge old pine, Coyote became aware of warmth, and a faint smell of singeing. Soon afterwards, a tiny piece of smouldering reed landed on the ground beside him. It had been blown there by the strong wind which came with each new moon. Coyote seized the reed, blew up a flame, and called to all his tribe. It was the first time that the Wintu had seen fire and they crowded round in excitement.

'Where can the burning reed have come from?' they asked. Everyone had an opinion, and during the discussion that followed, the flame, neglected, went out without anyone noticing! At last Grey Wolf, oldest of the tribe, stated that far away to the west, beyond the last great mountains, lay a mysterious land of fire. 'My father's father, Black Wolf, went there when he was very young,' said Grey Wolf.

'Tell me, Grey Wolf, why did Black Wolf not bring fire back to the Wintu?' asked Coyote.

'Because that was impossible for a single warrior. The journey to the Land of Fire is too long and too dangerous for someone to undertake on his own, and it is very difficult to bring back fire without it going out.'

Coyote thought for a long time then, a month later, an idea came to him. He invited the braves of the neighbouring tribes to join him. He particularly invited members of tribes whose totems were birds: eagles, falcons, hawks and crows. The group of warriors set out towards the sunset, crossing snowcapped mountains and fathomless ravines, but they never found the Land of Fire. They became tired and dispirited. Then Coyote sent off Red Falcon as a scout. Many Indians in that far-off time could take the

Coyote shows fire to the
Wintu women.

form of their totem animal, and the young brave turned himself into a red-winged bird of prey and rose up into the sky. Seven days later he returned empty handed.

Next Black Eagle took his turn as scout. He flew even farther and longer than Red Falcon. Just when he felt he must turn back his keen eye made out, far below, a thread of blue smoke. He was completely exhausted by the time he returned to tell his companions what he had seen. The Indians now sent the tiny Hummingbird to see what he could find out. He was so small that no one in the Land of Fire would notice him. So he flew off towards the sunset, while the others had a rest.

Two months later, when everyone had thought him lost, Hummingbird returned. Before he even landed he cried: 'I went to the ends of the earth and there, where land and sky touch, I saw a red glow beneath a column of blue smoke. I flew towards it without a sound – and it was indeed the Land of Fire!'

The end was in sight; but Hummingbird said that it would not be easy to get hold of some fire, for it was guarded by fierce warriors. What was more, the Land of Fire lay on top of a mountain lashed by waves, and surrounded on three sides by steep cliffs.

Coyote decided to use cunning. Without telling his friends what he meant to do, he made a long headdress of bark and dried leaves which came down to his shoulders and made him quite unrecognizable. Then he went up alone and unarmed to the entrance to the Land of Fire. In a quavering voice he said that he was just an old man who had lost his way in the mountains. The guards saw no reason not to believe him. They took him into their camp, where they ate, drank, and danced and sang all night. When dawn came and the guards slept, Coyote sidled up to the fire. He set light to an end of his bark headdress and ran off.

Just as Coyote was leaving the camp one of the guards saw him and raised the alarm. With beating heart, Coyote raced off as fast as he could, but his headdress got in his way and he

Between them, the warrior-birds carry fire back to their tribes.

tripped over a root. Several warriors flung themselves on him. One of the guards was waving Coyote's headdress in the air when Black Eagle swooped down from the clouds and seized it from him. Soon Red Falcon came to help him, then all the birds took turns in carrying it over the mountains – even Hummingbird, though the headdress was heavier than he! They reached their homeland before the fire died out.

The warriors were welcomed as heroes. Coyote had finally managed to shake off his pursuers and they all celebrated with a great feast. And ever since, the Wintu have cooked their food, warmed themselves in winter, and sung and danced around their fires.

▷ THE RED ISLAND ◁

The magic golden craft that Herakles had borrowed from Helios, the sun god, slipped silently through the waves. Herakles, the only man on board, scanned the horizon, for he was drawing near Erythia. Even he felt a shiver of nerves at the thought of landing on that dangerous island at the very edge of the world.

When Herakles sprang ashore, his heavy club on his shoulder, he was surprised to find that the cliffs, trees, soil, and even the birds were all red! Not far off, a vast herd of red oxen browsed in a field of red grass. Herakles was moving silently towards them when he was halted by a fierce growl. Orthrus, a huge dog, even larger than the oxen, sprang on him, his slavering lips drawn back to show fearsome fangs. Quick as lightning, Herakles stunned the beast with one blow of his club. The noise roused a shepherd called Eurytion. He rushed at Herakles, but was stunned in his turn.

At that moment a shrill scream curdled Herakles' blood. Another shepherd, Menoetes, was giving the alarm. His terrible cry roused the whole island. Almost at once the ground shook under the feet of Geryon, a giant with three bodies, three heads and six arms. He had come to chase the stranger from his land.

A violent fight followed. Herakles had to use all his weapons and call on all his skill to survive. He loosed an arrow into each of the three bodies, then struck each head a terrible blow with his club. But it was the next day before Herakles finally won the battle. He quickly rounded up a few oxen as proof that he had reached Erythia, and set sail. No one since has ever found the mysterious red island.

The red isle of Erythia provided the hero Herakles with several challenges.

BRITAIN

▷ THE ISLE OF GOLDEN APPLES ◁

Long ago, the Celts believed in a mysterious island, surrounded by steep cliffs and covered by forest. Delicious fruit grew on its trees, and flowers scented the air. Life was sweet on this strange island where night never fell.

The Celts believed that King Arthur, mortally wounded at the battle of Camlann, was carried to this island by Morgan le Fay and her seven sisters. Through the island ran rivers of wine, and trees bearing golden apples grew there. It was there that Arthur's magic sword Excalibur was forged. Only a few heroes such as Bran, Maelduin, Cormac and Arthur were able to visit the Isle of Golden Apples, where women were forever beautiful. Arthur never came back from it, though some still hope that one day he will.

CHINA
THE FLOATING ISLANDS

Chang held his old junk on course through the night, in spite of the rough waves and his growing unease. For he was nearing Kuei Hei, and had gone too far to turn back. A week earlier, his brother Wang had been delivering fish to the emperor's palace. There he had heard talk of a secret expedition to the mysterious islands of Kuei Hei – and so the brothers had set sail to reach the islands first.

Wang and Chang, like all Chinese sailors, had long dreamed of finding these mysterious floating islands, which drifted on the ocean, blown by the winds. Many people had caught a glimpse of the islands, but only a few had landed on them. They were known as the Happy Ones, for they never again felt hungry and never grew old. They wore garments of brilliant feathers, thanks to which they could fly.

Once there had been five floating islands, not three as there were now. Buffeted by the waves, they had crashed into one another and had even blown near to the dangerous reefs off the coast of the Middle Empire. The Happy Ones found this disturbing, and asked the Celestial Emperor to make their home more stable.

After some thought, the emperor sent five giant turtles to Kuei Hei, with orders to take the islands on their backs. Carrying an island is tiring work, so the emperor sent other turtles to help. There were three to each island and they took it in turns, one carrying the island while the others rested.

Chang knew this story but one point remained unclear. 'Did you learn at the palace why there are now only three floating islands?' he asked his brother. 'Yes!' said Wang. 'One

Carelessly the giant Long Po eats the turtles that carry the floating islands.

day the giant Long Po waded through the ocean and without warning scooped up six of the turtles and ate them. The two islands they looked after were blown to the frozen seas of the north, where they have iced over so that no one can live on them.'

Chang was remembering this when, at dawn, he realized that his ship was being swept along by a strong current. Suddenly the sky darkened, and he heard a groaning noise. A terrifying gulf opened in front of the junk. All the rivers on earth flowed into it, and each night the foaming waters of the Milky Way joined them from the sky. For hours the brothers battled desperately against the storm and the current, to avoid being sucked into the seething abyss.

The next day, worn out, Wang and Chang drifted into calm waters, but a thick fog enveloped them. They were sailing blindly through it when the mist briefly parted and they saw at last three islands, which floated lightly on the waves. With beating hearts they set a course for them.

Just as they neared the first island, it swerved and disappeared. The brothers turned towards the second, but as they were about to land, it too vanished! They could just make out the outline of the third through the fog, but as fast as they sailed towards it, it floated away. A strong north wind whipped up the waves and slowed their progress. Even so, with all sails set, they sped east after the island. But no one ever saw them again.

The bronze statue that guards the city of Jabal Lama.

▷ ALEXANDER'S SECRET CITY ◁

Jabal Lama was built thousands of years ago by one of Noah's sons. Constructed entirely of leather, the city had no less than forty palaces, surrounded by shady gardens. In the centre was the largest palace of all, topped by a shining dome. On the tip of the highest tower, on a round platform, a bronze knight stood guard. He launched his magic lance at strangers, which struck them down before they could even make a threatening gesture. In thirty centuries no one but Alexander the Great was ever allowed to enter Jabal Lama.

▷ THE CITY OF YS ◁

Long ago the splendid city of Ys stood proudly on the Atlantic coast of Brittany, in France. Although this wealthy city with its gilded palaces was below sea level, its people were not afraid, for high walls and strong gates protected it from the ocean. These gates were opened by a golden key which the king never let out of his hand. But one evening the king's daughter, who often gave wild parties, stole the golden key and handed it to one of her lovers. Soon after, the city was drowned by waves that swept through the streets, laying waste to everything in their path.

The princess, overcome by remorse, took the form of a mermaid and has wandered through the ocean ever since. Sometimes, when there is a particularly fierce storm, fishermen say that they have heard her sweet voice, and at the same time seen the towers of the drowned city emerge briefly from the waves.

The magnificent city of Ys is engulfed by the waves.

FRANCE

HUON OF BORDEAUX

Huon had travelled through many strange lands, and nothing could surprise him. But even he felt a thrill of excitement on the day he reached Femenie. The sun never rose on this shadowy country, whose inhabitants lived in perpetual half-light, stinking with sulphurous fumes. Huon pushed his horse on, followed by his companions. In the middle of a dusty plain, they came across a poor village. Seven thin, pale women seemed to be waiting for them there, but they did not speak. There were no men and no children to be seen, only a few mangy dogs that bared their teeth in silence. The knights did not linger in this sinister place, where even at dawn the cocks never crowed. They hurried on towards the mountains at the head of the valley, glad to see the back of Femenie.

A week later, as they reached the end of a stony track, light broke through the fog and they could see the sun reddening the horizon. A vast forest stretched as far as the eye could see. It looked peaceful, but Huon's attention was caught by sinister groans and crunching noises. He dismounted, drew his sword, and stealthily made his way into the woods. He peered through the leaves and saw, three paces ahead of him, a group of Koumans tearing into hunks of raw meat with their teeth, and gnawing the bones. These apemen growled like angry

Huon and his knights drive off the fearsome Koumans.

mastiffs. Their large, pointed ears twitched. Their skin was covered with hair as thick and coarse as that of a wild boar, and they loved to eat human flesh.

Brave as he was, even Huon shrank at the thought of being eaten! He beckoned his companions to come and see the creatures, and then began to creep away as quietly as possible. But the Koumans heard their steps and flung themselves on the knights, screaming, growling, and gnashing at them with their enormous pointed teeth.

Although the knights were outnumbered, the Koumans were not very brave, and were soon driven off by the knights' swords and lances. They hesitated to attack again. The knights closed ranks and charged, yelling, through a gap in the crowd of Koumans. Then they left the forest as quickly as they could.

At dawn Huon and his friends came to the Land of Faith. Its people were hardworking and honest. They grew delicious fruit, and enough corn and vegetables to feed the whole country. The knights stayed there to regain strength, but soon they set out again.

Beyond the Land of Faith, they came to a vast desert. It took them two months to cross it, and food and water ran short. Three knights and three horses died of exhaustion. The survivors were worn out when, at the far side of the desert, they came to a forest. In front of it waited a grey-haired hermit. He gave them a drink, and then guided them towards more adventures.

THE PERILOUS VALLEY

Alexander's army had won a series of victories over the Persians, but now the troops were lost in a maze of mountains. Suddenly the shrill neigh of Alexander's horse Bucephalus sounded the alarm through the valley. Immediately the advance guard halted. Thunder rumbled menacingly round the mountains as Bucephalus took a few more steps, then came to a halt before a smooth black cliff, on which appeared letters of fire. Alexander's companions gathered uneasily round their chief. At first no one could decipher the flaming letters, but Alexander remembered the lessons of the enchanter Nectanebus and the message became clear to him: 'No one leaves the Perilous Valley save he who dares to spend the whole night there alone.'

Alexander would let no one else stay in the valley, and after much argument persuaded his companions to withdraw at dusk, taking Bucephalus with them. He remained alone in the darkness. Towards midnight, a terrible storm broke. Lightning flashed and struck the ground a few paces from Alexander, leaving the bitter smell of sulphur. As if in a nightmare, he heard screams, and saw shadowy, monstrous shapes. Several times he thought he saw the devil. Towards daybreak his fears were lifting when a last bolt of lightning struck the cliff behind him. A shower of rocks fell, then came an inhuman, bloodcurdling scream. As light strengthened Alexander made out the form of the devil, crushed under a rock brought down by the lightning – caught in his own trap!

The devil promised to give Alexander whatever he wanted in return for his release, and the Greek asked simply for the means of leaving the

Perilous Valley. 'Right!' said the devil. 'But the only way out passes through the Land of the Otifals.'

The next day, Alexander rejoined Bucephalus and his companions and they set out. Following the direction the devil had pointed out, they soon came to a swift-flowing river. Just as they were starting to ford it, their horses reared and refused to go on. A huge monster rose from the waters. Its head was a cross between a dog and a bull, and a foul stench came from its gaping mouth. Its huge body, larger than that of an elephant, was covered in limp folds of skin so thick that no weapon could pierce it. This was an Otifal! The screeching monster gobbled up several horses and their riders. The others fought until evening, and then withdrew.

As they were wondering what to do, three water nymphs appeared. They lived in the waters of the Valley of the Three Fountains – the Fountain of Life, the Fountain of Youth, and the Fountain of Immortality. They guided the brave knights to a stone bridge that allowed them to cross over the great river. A week later, they made their way out of the Land of the Otifals and arrived before the Trees of the Sun and the Moon – magic trees that signalled the approaching end of Alexander's life. But the young king did not believe them, and continued his adventurous journey.

The Otifal rises from the river to confront Alexander and his men.

PERSIA

CITY OF GOLD

Long ago a beautiful golden-eyed princess lived in the heart of the Kingdom of the Indies. She was clever and beautiful, but she had never married. She had seen off a crowd of suitors, including princes, but said that she would marry the man, be he prince or pauper, who was brave enough to enter the City of Gold.

No one knew exactly where the City of Gold was. Some said that a group of sailors, driven off course by a storm, had seen it beyond the ocean, on the coast of an unknown land. All its buildings were said to be made of precious metals and jewels, and even the streets were paved with gold.

Saktideva hid as a giant Garoura landed on the magic fig tree.

Many men set out on the quest, but none returned. Despite this, a fisherman's son called Saktideva decided to take up the challenge. He was barely twenty years old, but he knew the seas better than most, and like many fishermen he was brave and hardy. With six companions he set sail in secret.

After several uneventful days, the skies suddenly clouded over and a fearful storm broke, more violent than any Saktideva had ever known. In just a few minutes the boat was broken up and everything in it tossed into the sea. Half drowned, Saktideva clung to a spar and drifted through the night. When day dawned, he thought he was dreaming. Strange leaves, as big as boats, were floating on the waves around him. With the last of his strength, Saktideva hauled himself on to one. For the time being, he was safe.

When he felt able to look around him, Saktideva saw that his leaf was attached to a long branch, so long that he could not see its end until the storm and the waves died down. At last he made out the trunk of a fig tree, higher than a mountain, rising from the ocean bed. For more than an hour Saktideva climbed up from branch to branch, hoping to see land on the horizon. But he was worn out by his ordeal and fell asleep in a hole in the trunk. At dawn, cold and hunger woke him and he started to climb once more. But he could see no trace of his boat, nor of his companions, and no sign of land. He was alone in the middle of the ocean, but at least he could eat figs to satisfy his hunger!

At dusk Saktideva settled down to spend his second night in the giant tree, but he was too worried to sleep. Suddenly he heard a loud noise in the west, and the setting sun was blotted out by a flock of monstrous birds that wheeled towards him. They were the Garouras. Screaming shrilly, they settled on the tree around him. Saktideva nearly died of fright, but the darkness hid him from the birds. As he sheltered in the crook of a branch, just above the feathers of an enormous Garoura, he realized that it provided him with his only chance of escape. So in the depths of night, when the great bird was asleep, he slid on to its back. It stirred and scratched its feathers. Its sharp claws raked across Saktideva but then it yawned and settled down again.

At dawn the flock of Garouras took flight straight towards the rising sun. Saktideva hung on for dear life, although the wind whistled past him, and after one horrified look at the sea far below he had to shut his eyes. Luckily the giant bird seemed unaware of its passenger, and a few hours later the flock flew over the gleaming domes of a sparkling city – the City of Gold!

One by one the Garouras landed. The citizens hardly looked up, so the monsters were clearly a familiar sight. Saktideva's bird landed in the middle of a quiet garden full of flowers, a few paces from a magnificent palace. The young man slipped to the ground as quietly as possible, but a gardener saw him. He told him that he was in the Forbidden City, the home of a great princess. At that moment she came into the garden, and when she looked at him Saktideva realized that she was the princess of the golden eyes! 'How did you come here?' she asked. 'On the back of this bird,' Saktideva stammered. 'The Garouras are messengers, not birds,' said the princess, 'and why have you come?'

'Because I want to marry you, as you promised you would,' replied the young man frankly. The princess looked at him up and down in silence, and after a time said, 'Because of my promise and your courage, I may accept you. But don't rejoice too soon. First I must talk to my father.' She gave him her hand to kiss, then flew off on the back of a Garoura.

While he waited for her return, Saktideva was brought magnificent clothes and all he wanted

to eat. He was allowed to roam over almost all the palace except for the great terrace.

For six days Saktideva waited patiently but the princess did not come back. On the seventh day he could not resist climbing the staircase to the great terrace, and to his surprise found himself in a huge garden. In its centre was a pool so still and clear that it reflected the blue sky like a

The white horse carrying Saktideva sprang into the pool on the great terrace.

mirror. Nearby stood a white horse. He went over to stroke it, then sprang on to its back. Immediately it leaped into the centre of the pool. The surface exploded into thousands of crystal drops which formed themselves into a whirlpool. Saktideva was sucked into it, and lost consciousness.

Next day he woke to find himself at home!

His friends told him that he had been shipwrecked and found unconscious on the shore. No one would believe his tales of the Garouras and the City of Gold – it must have been a dream. But was it not curious that everyone had seen a strange and beautiful white horse on the beach where he was found, and that Saktideva was dressed in clothes fit for a prince?

▷ ATLANTIS ◁

The beautiful young orphan Clito lived alone on a large island, far beyond the Pillars of Herakles. For months she cried such bitter tears that at last Poseidon, the great god of the sea, was moved by her distress and her beauty. He decided to marry her, and they set up home on a hillside overlooking the sea. But Poseidon found the island boring and uncomfortable and decided to improve it. With all the energy of a god in love, he worked day and night, until by the ninth day the island was unrecognizable. Poseidon had encircled it with a high wall. Next he built two deep moats, enclosed by two more walls. The island of Atlantis had taken shape.

Poseidon and Clito spent many happy days on Atlantis and had five pairs of twins – ten

Poseidon the sea god turned the island of Atlantis into a fortress for his family.

boys, the eldest of whom they called Atlas. When they grew up, the island was divided into ten parts, one for each son and his descendants.

A great canal allowed ships to pass through the first two walls and gain access to the central island, and fortified bridges formed an easy way from one ring to another. In the centre of the city, on a marble hill, the Atlantans built magnificent palaces of white, black and red stone. A temple dedicated to Poseidon and Clito, protected by walls of gold, dominated the whole island.

At first the Atlantans were sober and hard-working, excellent sailors and farmers and brave warriors. But sadly, little by little, they embarked on foreign conquests, pillaging, and a life of pleasure. The great god Zeus, watching from Mount Olympus, became displeased with them. Flying into a terrible rage, he caused a great earthquake, together with a tidal wave so high that it swept over the three rings of walls, and drowned the magnificent city. Since that far-off time, somewhere under the ocean, sleep the ruins of once-brilliant Atlantis.

LEGEND OR HISTORY?

Over the centuries people have explored the farthest corners of the world, driven by curiosity, greed, or just the love of adventure. Little by little they have overcome all fears and obstacles to enlarge the frontiers of known lands. At the start of this century, only Tibet, the Hoggar Desert, the polar regions, the heights of the Andes Mountains and the heart of the Amazon forests were still mysterious lands, known only from rumours and garbled stories. They were the last blank spaces on the map over which the imagination could range freely. Distance, dangers, or extremes of climate protected them from the rational explanations of geographers and scientists. They were said to be inhabited by strange people of whom extraordinary stories were told, similar to legends which had been told since ancient times – for great civilizations have always felt themselves surrounded by barbarians and mysterious lands.

Egyptian Punt and mysterious Ophir

The Egyptians sent many expeditions by sea to look for gold and incense. The name Punt was used for a far-off country which was difficult to reach. Historians have been able to find out little about it; they only know that Egyptian sailors voyaged throughout the Red Sea by about 1500 BC. Sometimes they place Punt on the Yemen coast, sometimes in East Africa. The Egyptians, like all the great travellers of ancient times, kept their routes across the sea a closely guarded secret, especially when these led to sources of precious stones and metals and other valuable goods.

Whether they wished it or not, the stories of far-off countries gave rise to extravagant rumours; these were welcomed, as by emphasizing the dangers and telling of monsters they put off other travellers. But sometimes these rumours were based on actual events that were exaggerated into legends as they were retold.

This tomb painting from the Valley of the Kings, near Egyptian Thebes, shows a sailing ship. The Egyptians were great explorers but kept their routes a closely guarded secret.

This may be how the legend of the mysterious kingdom of Ophir grew up in the East around 945 BC. We find it mentioned in the Bible, in the Book of Kings. There we learn that Phoenician sailors of King Hiram of Tyre, on ships built for King Solomon, reached a marvellously rich land called Ophir. From this land, whose whereabouts were unknown but which is similar in many respects to Egyptian Punt, they brought back gold, silver, ivory, monkeys, peacocks and slaves. Hiram's expedition probably left the Gulf of Akkaba and sailed south, but from there on there is no actual trace of it, despite many rumours. Explorers and adventurers have never stopped looking for the site of Ophir, but in vain. Some scholars have even suggested that it might have been in America!

Where does the sun live?

In its apparent journey around the earth, the sun disappears every day from sight. This has given birth to the deep-rooted belief that it rests – or perhaps hides – during the night. The Egyptians believed that the sun god Ra journeyed all night through the Underworld on a boat, before rising the next morning. The Greeks had rather the same idea, thinking that at night the sun god Helios abandoned his chariot and took to a golden bowl to travel underground. According to the Aztecs, the sun spent the night in a palace. Once astronomers had demonstrated that it was the earth that went round the sun, this sort of belief died out, but the legends remain.

The Greeks and Romans

First the Greeks and then the Romans added greatly to the stories of mysterious lands. These were often placed on the edge of the Mediterranean, outside the world with which they were familiar. Stories attributed to Homer (from eight or nine centuries BC) tell of giants and cyclops living in far islands, and of goddesses and magicians who lived in countries whose common characteristic was that they were far from Greece. The Lands of the Setting Sun, in the great ocean west of the Pillars of Herakles (the Straits of Gibraltar) were the scene of many strange adventures. These lands included Erythia, the red island which Herakles reached in Helios's golden craft. Greek legends also told of the frozen and unknown countries of northern Europe, such as Hyperborea, which is shown on maps attributed to Herodotus dating from about 400 BC. Thule, 'the most northern of the lands of the North', towards which Pytheas of Marseilles sailed in about 325 BC, is placed sometimes in Norway and sometimes in Iceland.

In the 4th century BC the philosopher Plato gave plenty of food for thought to lovers of mystery when he described the brilliant civilization of Atlantis. Sadly Plato gave no means of placing it in time or space.

Drowned lands and cities

Over the centuries the world became better known and then better mapped. However, people's imagination still clung to the unknown. So the Celts believed for a long time in worlds similar to their own but lying beneath the waters, in the great Irish lakes or hidden at the bottom of the sea. These could rarely be seen, and then only by those privileged to pass unharmed between one world and another.

In Brittany, a stronghold of Celtic culture, there are many variations on the theme of the drowned city and the disappearance of the city of Ys. A Christian version includes the intervention of the devil and of Saint Gwenole, and is probably based on an earlier Celtic, pre-Christian story. The idea of cities disappearing beneath the sea probably comes from the fact that over the centuries parts of the coasts of Brittany, Scotland and Ireland have disappeared under the persistent onslaughts of the waves.

Monsters and enchanters

In the West, the Middle Ages were particularly rich in tales of strange countries. The stories of actual travellers, such as Marco Polo (1254-1324) in his *Book of the Wonders of the World,* and of armchair travellers, such as John of Mandeville (who died in Liège in 1372), were inextricable mixtures of fact and fiction. Over several centuries Mandeville's books were translated into several languages, and often retold; they were successful throughout Europe.

Plato and Atlantis

The theme of Atlantis, the mysterious kingdom suddenly drowned, has been the inspiration for literature for over 2000 years. The earliest clear references to it are in the works of the Greek philosopher and teacher Plato, in the 4th century BC. Although he does not devote much space to it, Plato speaks of Atlantis as an ideal state, built on a fabulous island, which had been set up around 9000 years before he wrote. Was he using it to represent his ideal sort of organization, or was he truly describing a state which had disappeared, and of which some vague and garbled memories had been passed down? Some 2400 years later, it is impossible to say.

People have long and vainly sought for any trace of Atlantis in the Mediterranean, in the Azores and the Canaries. Those who still think it may once have existed are now considering the Greek island of Santorini. It was half destroyed by a volcanic explosion around 1500 BC, which also considerably damaged the rich and flourishing cities of Crete and hastened the end of a sophisticated pre-Greek civilization around the Aegean Sea. The theme of Atlantis could well reflect this ancient catastrophe, but at the same time its story of the destruction of a people who became too proud and overbearing is one that is eternally popular. The truth is never likely to be known.

What remains of the island of Santorini.

Part of a 16th-century map of Scandinavia, showing legendary monsters in the north Atlantic Ocean. (J.-L. Charmet)

Purporting to describe actual far-off countries, these books and many others like them told of strange Eastern kingdoms peopled by monsters and with bizarre customs. The medieval tales of chivalry also described mysterious countries. The adventures of Arthur and Merlin were set in a world that was near but just as mysterious as those far off: the world of enchanters. There, as in the lands of older Celtic legends, there were vast forests where one could stray into the Valley of No Return, nameless fortresses and men who never grew old.

The Europeans of the Middle Ages were not completely duped into thinking that these were real places, but they liked to believe that, far from home and everyday life, at the very edge of the known world, were two-headed men, trees that could talk, and enchanting princesses.

Paradise on earth

Even up to the 20th century people were still looking for an earthly Paradise. Living in harsh conditions, they wanted to believe in far countries, hidden from almost everyone, which were nearly impossible to reach. This theme is deep rooted in Celtic culture, where heroes such as Bran, Maelduin and Brandon braved all dangers to reach the marvellous lands of the West. In those far-off islands there were no seasons; it was always warm, and beautiful women, eternally young, smiled on the brave. The same idea crops up in many civilizations. In ancient China, Paradise also lay in distant and almost inaccessible regions – the highest peaks of the mountains of the West, or the far

The ice that covers the polar regions was another source of legends. (G. Robertson/ Jacana)

islands of the Pacific Ocean. The frozen peaks of the Himalayas remained unconquered until the middle of this century, and so it was possible to think of them as the home of the 'Great Empress of the West', whose jade palace dominated the world.

In the Middle Ages, Chinese junks sailed the Pacific and landed on many islands, but it was very difficult to place these precisely since there was no proper system of latitude or longitude. An island might be found several times in apparently different places, while another might seem to have disappeared from its expected location. This gave rise to the idea of floating islands, which is particularly widespread in China, and is also found in ancient Greece.

Precious cities

The ancient Chinese thought that the high mountains to the west, whose summits reached more than 8000 metres, formed the boundary of the world, where were built magnificent palaces of jade. Other civilizations similarly told of cities entirely built of strange and precious materials. The Arabs and people of the Sahara, who were familiar with salt lakes and strange rock formations, imagined cities and palaces of crystal, probably inspired by desert mirages. Europeans were fascinated by precious metals, and envisaged cities of gold at the edge of the world. In the same way, found in cartoon books and science fiction. But now, rather than placing them on earth, even the remotest regions of which are too well known, authors of science fiction or simply of fantasy place them in imaginary civilizations parallel to those on earth, as did H.G. Wells in his *War of the Worlds*. Others describe strange cities on the moon and – since it became too well known – on the planet Mars or still farther planets. Others have taken up the theme of Atlantis, imagining for instance that its people

had survived the cataclysm and formed an underground civilization.

The essential point of these stories of mysterious and unexplored 'lands' is that they give rise to dreams. In retelling the tales of antiquity and the Middle Ages, these authors have revived ancient legends and adapted them to the taste of our times. For the wish to escape from the everyday world to a time and place of fantasy is as strong today as it has ever been.

These strange formations sculptured by the winds and sand of the desert may have given rise to some tales of great and long-lost cities. (Zefa-Damm)

in the 16th century, there were many rumours of El Dorado, the city of gold, in the newly discovered Americas.

Legends for today

As more and more of the world became known, imaginary lands became even more fantastic. Authors wrote of regions forgotten by time, in which dinosaurs still lived, or of undersea worlds. The old themes of lost cities, cities outside time, cities of leather, crystal or metal, underground and underwater cities have gained new momentum in the 20th century. New lands of mystery are

The Kingdom of Shangri-la

Tibet was one of the very last regions to be explored by Europeans, and many legends grew up about it. Perhaps the best known is that of Shangri-la, the name given to an almost inaccessible valley in the Tibetan mountains in which was a strange monastery. There a few wise men devoted their time to meditation, and the preservation of

all that was best in the arts and culture. They were able to slow down the effects of time, so that as long as they remained in Shangri-la they could stay young for centuries; if ever they left, they instantly aged. James Hilton told the story of Shangri-la in his novel *Lost Horizon*; it was made into a popular film in 1937. The story is a later version of the legends of a land of Eternal Youth, well known to the Celts and the Chinese.

Many Chinese legends tell of great palaces built high on mountain peaks. (Explorer/L. Girard)

▷ INDEX ◁